→ Joyce   Johnson

Webs and Wheels

readingbasics**plus**

HARPER & ROW, PUBLISHERS NEW YORK   HAGERSTOWN   SAN FRANCISCO   LONDON

CONTRIBUTORS

DOLORES R. AMATO   LYNETTE SAINE GAINES   JOSEPH A. LUCERO
A. DICKSON CARROLL   ERIC P. HAMP   MATTIE CLAYBROOK WILLIAMS
CHERIE A. CLODFELTER   PHILLIP L. HARRIS

Special acknowledgment to Sister Colette Zirbes and Marilyn Buckley Hanf.

ACKNOWLEDGMENTS

"A bear went over the mountain" from *The Rooster Crows, A Book of American Rhymes and Jingles* by Maud and Miska Petersham. Copyright 1945 by The Macmillan Company. Reprinted by courtesy of Macmillan Publishing Co., Inc., New York.

"I'm really not lazy" from *A Rumbudgin of Nonsense* by Arnold Spilka. Copyright © 1970 by Arnold Spilka. Reprinted by permission of Charles Scribner's Sons, New York.

An adaptation of *Sabrina* by Martha Alexander. Copyright © 1971 by Martha Alexander. Adapted by permission of The Dial Press, New York.
"A skunk is a skunk is a skunk" from *A Rumbudgin of Nonsense* by Arnold Spilka. Copyright © 1970 by Arnold Spilka. Reprinted by permission of Charles Scribner's Sons, New York.

"Tracks," adapted from pp. 12-18 of *How To Be a Nature Detective* by Millicent Selsam. Text copyright © 1958, 1963 by Millicent Selsam. Adapted by permission of Harper & Row, Publishers, Inc., New York.

EDITORS MARGUERITE LISTON, SHERRE B. LEVENE, GERRY JUNG ELAINE S. GOLDBERG, DIANE K. LINDEMAN, SYLVIA J. ROSENSTEIN

DIRECTING EDITORS MARTHA A. HAYES and EDDY JO BRADLEY

DESIGN BARBARA WASSERMAN, KRISTIN NELSON

ILLUSTRATION BILL ANDERSON and JUDY ANDERSON pages 6-12, 13-18, 82-85; KINUKO Y. CRAFT pages 20-24, 39-44, 50-56, 86-87, 134-138; DAVID CUNNINGHAM pages 64-70, 140-145; JOHN DOWNS pages 120-126, 156-160; JOHN FREAS pages 57, 102, 103; LIONEL KALISH pages 46, 80, 81, 116, 117; CARL KOCK cover, pages 25, 26, 63, 94, 95, 118, 119, 132, 133; BOB MASHERIS pages 5, 45, 46, 79-81, 115-117; BILL MORRISON pages 35-38, 47-49, 104-110, 127-131; JERRY PINKNEY pages 27-33, 71-77, 146-153; TOM UPSHUR pages 19, 78, 139; JACK WALLEN pages 34, 88-93, 154-155.

PHOTOGRAPHY CBS NEWS pages 111, 112, 113, 114; RON CHURCH (Tom Stack and Associates) page 99; RON DILLOW (Tom Stack and Associates) page 62; DICK HANLEY (Photo Researchers, Inc.) page 39; KARL W. KENYON pages 96, 97, 101; ROBERT McKENDRICK page 62; FRANKLIN McMAHON pages 58, 60, 61, 62; TOM MYERS (Tom Stack and Associates) page 98; LOREN LEWIS (Tom Stack and Associates) page 59; WIDE WORLD PHOTOS pages 40, 41, 42, 43, 44; CLEM G. WIEDMAN (Tom Stack and Associates) page 59.

CONTENTS

Looking at TV

"Sono, come out here," said Mom.
"Kit is here, and I am going out.
You and Tad can play here, but do
not put on the TV.
I want to be here when you look at TV.
Kit will be here with you."

"OK, Mom," said Sono.

"I wish we could look at TV," said Tad.

"I do, too.
  But we can't," said Sono.
"Mom said we could not.
  So that is that."

7

"Sono, we can put the TV on," said Tad.
"Kit will not have to know."

"Tad, do not start that," said Sono.
"My mom will not like it."

"Then what can we do?" said Tad.

"I know," said Sono. "We can make a TV."

"We can?" said Tad.

"It will not be hard," said Sono.
"We can make a TV.
  Then we can look at TV and be on TV."

"Sono, I am here now," said Mom.
"What are you doing?"

"We are looking at TV," said Sono.

"I said that I did not want
you to put on the TV," said Mom.

"You said we could not put
on that TV," said Sono.
"So we made this TV.
And it is fun.
How do you like this TV?
Come and be on TV with Tad."

Tim and the Tacos

"Can you come to
my house?" Meg said.
"We are going to have tacos."

taco

"I'll go and
ask Mom," said Pat.

"My mother said OK," said Pat.
"So we can come, Meg.
   Come on, Tim."

"First, I want to know what
tacos are," said Tim.

taco

"You do not have to ask," said Meg.
"You will find out."

Tim thought, "What are
tacos like?

taco

I like the things my mother makes.

I do not like new things.

But I do not want Meg's mother to

be mad at me.

What will I do?"

tacos

table

"Here we are, Mom," said Meg.

"Good," said Mrs. López.
"The tacos are on the table.
 Ask Pat and Tim to come in."

taco

"I am going to like
tacos," said Pat.

"You would," Tim thought.

"Do you want some, Tim?" asked Meg.

Tim thought, "I'll have some.

I have to.

I do not want her to find out that

I don't want <u>tacos</u>."

taco

Tim had some tacos.

"This is good, Mrs. López," Tim said.

"I did not think I would like

tacos, but I do."

skunk

mouse

snake

elephant

A skunk is a skunk is a skunk

and a mouse is a

mouse mouse mouse mouse mouse.

A snake is a

SSS — NNNNNAAAAA — KE

And an elephant

IS.

19

spider

The Web

The little <u>spider</u> said, "I would
like to make a web.
But it is not fun.
It is hard work.
I think I'll ask for help.
Everyone will help."

A puppy came by.

"Will you help me make my web?" asked the spider.

spider

"I like to do new things," said the puppy. "It looks like fun, but I don't know how. What is a web made of?"

A little cat came by.

The <u>spider</u> asked, "Will
you help me make my web?"

spider

The cat said, "You would ask that!
I know how to climb a tree, but
I don't know how to make a web.
I wish I did.
I would like to.
A web looks like a puff of hair."

Then a ladybug came by.

"Will you help me make my web?" the spider asked.

spider

ladybug

"Not me," said the ladybug.
"I can fly a little.
I am good to my grandmother and my children.
But I can't make a web."

23

"That is it.
I'll have to make my
web," thought the little spider.

spider

ladybug

"But that is OK!
A puppy can't make a web.
A cat can't make a web.
A ladybug can't make a web.
It is something not everyone can do.
But I can!
I can make a web," she thought.

24

When Did You Learn This?

When did you learn how to think?

Where do you do your thinking?

How did you learn your name?

When did you learn it?

When did you learn how to
make a wish?

When did you learn how to play?

When did you learn how to
climb a tree?

Did You Learn This in School?

Did you learn how to fly in school?

If so, how do you do it?

Where did you learn how to work?

Did you learn how to be happy?

What do you do to be happy?

Did you learn how to hit a fly?

If so, where do you do that?

At Night

It was night.

Sam was at Dan's house.

Dan's cat was playing.

He was climbing on Dan.

"Just look at him play," said Sam.

"What can we do to have fun?"

Sam thought and thought.

So did Dan.

"I know what," thought Dan.

"I'll think of something to make Sam afraid.
  It is a good night for that."

"I know," thought Sam.

"I'll think of something to make Dan afraid.
  It is a good night for that."

"Dan, did you see that?" asked Sam.

"Here it comes.

It is something big.

It is going to climb in.

Do you see it?"

"I do," said Dan.

"I can hear it, too.

Can you hear it, Sam?

Can you see it?

Something is here.

What do you think it is?"

"I don't know," said Sam.

"But I think I can hear and see it.

Do you think it will walk in here?

I don't like this night.

Are you afraid like me?"

"Sam," said Dan,

"we are just seeing and hearing things.

When we started, it was for fun.

So when we stop playing, we

will stop being afraid."

"OK," said Sam.
"I am not playing now.
But I can't stop being afraid.
I wish I could."

"I am like you," said Dan.
"I know what we can do.
We can laugh.
We will not be afraid when we
are laughing."

Happy

I am very happy
Don't you see?
A cup of milk
Just for me.

I am very happy
Don't you see?
A big, big laugh
Just for me.

Where Is the Sun?

Would you look at this mud!
When will this rain stop?

We have to do something!
We have to have a truck.

What good would
a truck do?

We could put
this mud in it.

36

Here comes a truck!

Can we ask you to stop?
We want to put this mud in.

I wish the rain would stop. Where is the sun?

The sun was in the truck. And you know what you will have to do to get it out.

38

THE CIRCUS

circus

The Circus

Some children live with a circus.
They have mothers and dads who
work for the circus.
They learn how to do things in the
circus when they are little.
Then everyone can be in the
circus when the circus plays.

circus

The children who live with a circus
go to school, too.
Some children go to a school like
your school.
Some children go to a school in the circus.
They learn things that you learn.
They talk and play just like you do.

circus

Children can go to a circus school, too.
In this school they find out how
to do a circus act.
They work hard at this school.
The children want to do a good act so
they can work in a circus.

Some children want to be <u>clowns</u>.

They can go to a school for clowns.

At this school they find out how to

look like clowns.

clowns

They learn how to act like <u>clowns</u>.

They learn how to talk like clowns.

When they get out of school, they can be in the <u>circus</u>.

Then they can make everyone laugh and have fun.

circus clowns

circus

Children who live with a
circus have fun and work hard.

Some children do not live with a
circus, but they go to a circus school.

Would you like to be in a circus?
What would you do?

Collection 2

Words You Can Read

bridge

picture

snow

telephone

track

van

woman

48

49

A Good Nap

A man walked up to me.

"I'm Nat," he said.
"What is your name?"

"I'm Will," I said.

"I'm just going to eat.

Would you like to eat with me?" I asked.

"I think I'll do that," he said.

So we sat down.

When the man sat down, he put
something inside a hat.

"What would a man put inside a
hat?" I thought.
"I'm going to ask him."

We started to eat.

I thought I could hear something.

I thought I could hear a little cry.

The little cry came from inside the hat!

It was a cry for help!

"Help!

Help!"

Just then a little man climbed
out of the hat.

"I don't like to live in that hat.
I'm happy to be out.
It is not fun to be inside a hat.
Did you hear my cry?
You are very good to help me," he said.

"But I did not help," I said.

54

"Will!
Will!" said my mother.
"Did you have a good nap?"

Can You Say This?

Pat pulled the puppy.

Would Will want to walk on a web?

Did you say that Sam said she was so sad?

He hid her hat in the house.

What Can a **Picture** Say?

Pictures can talk to you.

They can say things.

Look at this picture.

It is saying that the

children like milk.

Is that what it is saying to you?

This milk is good.

We like milk.

What do the <u>pictures</u> say?

A <u>bridge</u> can be very big.

A bridge can be very little.

The pictures say that some bridges are big and some are little.

What do the pictures say?

The <u>woman</u> is running hard.

The woman came in first.

The pictures say that the
woman ran hard and she came in first.

What do the pictures say?

Do not go on the <u>track</u> now.

Now you can go, but look up and
down the track first.

The pictures say when to go on the tracks.

I'm sad.

I make a web.

I'm happy.

I live in the zoo.

Can You Do This?

Alexander Graham Bell

Alexander Graham Bell worked hard.

He made pictures for some people.

The people could not hear and
could not talk.

He helped the people learn how to talk.

Alexander Graham Bell came to
America to show people the pictures.

"I'm going to a school for
people who can't hear," he said.
"The pictures can
help people learn to talk."

Bell's pictures helped many
people learn how to talk.
Then Alexander Graham Bell did
something to help people who
could hear and talk.

"I think I could make something that
will help everyone," he thought.

He worked with Thomas Watson.
They worked very hard and
made many things.
But they did not make one
thing that worked.

"I just know we can make
something good," said Alexander.
"We will just have to work and work."

66

One night they made something that worked.

Alexander was in one room in the house.

Thomas Watson was not in the room.

Alexander said, "Come here. I want you."

Thomas could hear what Alexander said.
He could hear Alexander talk with
something they had made.

Thomas and Alexander had made
the first telephone.
People came to see the telephone.
They thought it was a good
thing to play with.
It was fun to talk on the telephone.
But they did not know a
telephone could help everyone.

Alexander Graham Bell talked to
many people.

"The telephone will help everyone," he said.
"I will show how my telephone works.
Everyone will want to have one."

And people did want telephones.
They wanted telephones in the
house and at work.

Alexander Graham Bell was happy.

People wanted the telephone he made.

But he did not stop working to
help people.

He went to a school for people who
could not hear.

He helped the people learn to talk.

"I'm very, very happy now," said Bell.

"I'm doing what I want to do, and
I'm helping people, too."

I Don't Want to Move!

Everyone was working hard at
the Smith house.
They had things to do.
By night they would be in a
big, new house.
The old house was too little.
Mother was very happy.
Dad was happy, too.
But Sharon was not happy.

"It is no fun to move," thought Sharon.
"I will not see Mark and

Barbara and everyone at school.

I don't want to go where I don't

know everyone.

And no one asked me if

I wanted to move.

If they had asked me, I know what I

would have said.

I would have

said no."

Sharon's mother came into the room.

"You look mad," she said.
"How come?"

"I am mad," said Sharon.
"No one asked me if I wanted to move.
I do not want to.
It is fun to live here.
It's not fun to move."

"You will be happy to move.
You will see," said Mrs. Smith.

"Not me," thought Sharon.

73

Sharon's dad was putting
out things to eat.

"Would you like something to
eat, Sharon?" said Mr. Smith.

"No, Dad. I'm not
going to eat now," said Sharon.

"You look like you
are going to cry," said Mr. Smith.

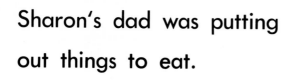

"I am not going to cry!" said Sharon.
"I am going to Barbara's house.
She asked me to come to her house."

Sharon looked at a big tree.

"I think I will just climb up here and
let everyone look for me," she thought.
"Then they can not move.
But Barbara will be mad if I do not
go to her house now.
She has something for me."

So Sharon ran to
Barbara's house.

Sharon walked up to Barbara's house.
She thought she could hear
children laughing when she went inside.
No one was in the room but Barbara.

"I am hearing things," Sharon thought.

"I'm sad that you have to move," said Barbara.

"Me, too!
And it's so far from
here," said Sharon.

"I know.
But it's not far from my
grandmother's house," said Barbara.
"I will go to see her and to see you.
Come on, Sharon.
I have something to show you."

"Surprise! Surprise!" everyone said.

Then everyone was talking to Sharon.

"We are sad that you are going," said Mark.
"But we have something for you in here.
It's something for you to
play with in your new house."

Sharon looked inside.
She could see a puppy.

"I am happy and sad inside," said Sharon.
"But I think it will be OK to move now."

First Snow

The first snow comes down,
Flying across the houses,
And finding my hand.

Collection 3

Words You Can Read

cake

chain

escalator

ice

ice cream

rock

sea otter

steps

wheels

Words You Can Read

a	o	e	u
clams	pot	set	pup
crack	hop	beds	duck's
	lots	them	
	got	red	
		wet	

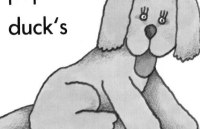

stop + p + ed   stopped
pop + p + ed   popped

1	2	3	4
one	two	three	four

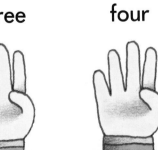

An Escalator

This is an escalator.

An escalator is a

set of steps.

You do not walk up and

down the steps.

This <u>step</u> can move you.
It is like a little truck with
little <u>wheels</u>.
The little wheels of the step
move on a track.

Inside an escalator are big wheels.

The big wheels move.

The wheels move a chain.

This chain pulls the
steps on the track.

When you go up, the
chain pulls the steps up.
Then the steps go
down inside the escalator.

When you go down, the
chain pulls the steps down.
Then it pulls them up inside
the escalator.

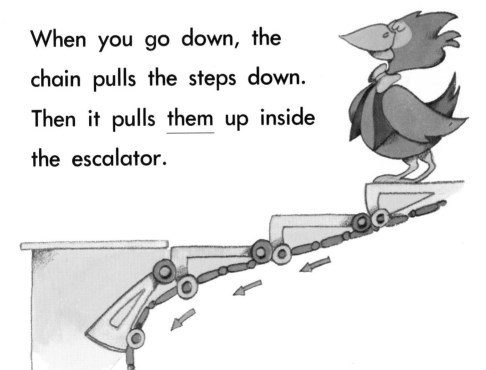

Up in the Sky

Look!
Up in the sky.
What do you see
Walking across the night?
What do you hear
Crying, then laughing?

Look!
It stops to think a little.

Now it knows
What to do.
Again it rides in,
Crying and laughing.
Can you see it,
Can you hear it,
Sock the sky?

Just Looking

Puff sat in a tree and looked at the sky.

"What a beautiful sky!" he thought.
"I will not go to school.
I'll sit here and look at the sky."

So he did not move.

Everyone but Puff went to school.

"Are you going to school?" asked
Little Red.

Puff just sat and looked.

When school was over, Laughing Cat
talked to Little Red.

"Puff was not at school," said
Laughing Cat.
"That was a surprise."

"I know," said Little Red.
"He is up in a tree looking at the sky.
 I don't know when he will
 come out of that tree again."

The day was over.

When night came, Puff sat in the tree.

Again night came and went.

The next day Puff sat and looked at the

sun move across the sky.

Everyone was going to school.
They could see Puff in the tree.

"Come on to school!" they said.
"We are going to have a surprise.
We are going to see how
ice cream is made.
Then everyone will get to eat some."

Puff thought and thought.

"I do like ice cream!
But I like looking at
the sky, too!
What will I do?" he said.

"I do not have to sit in a tree to see.
I can eat ice cream and look at the sky.
Eating ice cream in school will be fun."

So Puff came down out of the tree.
He went to school.

On a Walk

The children are going for a walk.

Who will have to walk in mud?
Who will walk by his school?
Who can stop for ice cream?
Who will have to climb over a wheel?

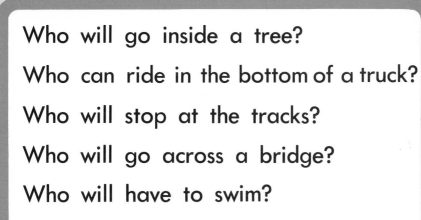

Who will go inside a tree?

Who can ride in the bottom of a truck?

Who will stop at the tracks?

Who will go across a bridge?

Who will have to swim?

Who can play in the snow?

The **Sea** **Otter**

The sea otter is an animal that
lives in the sea.
Sea otters eat and play in the sea.

96

The sea otter's back feet
are like a duck's feet.
They help it swim.
The feet go up and down.
This helps the sea otter swim.

Sea otters have beds.

The beds are not like people's beds.

They are made of something that

lives in the sea.

It is kelp.

A mother sea otter puts her pup in a kelp

bed when she looks for something to eat.

When sea otters
want something to eat,
they swim down to
the bottom of the sea.
They like the
things that live on
the bottom of the sea.
They like clams and
things like that.

A sea otter finds
a clam to eat.
Then it looks for
a rock.
It comes up with
the clam and
the rock.

The rock will help the
sea otter crack the clam.
The sea otter swims on its
back and puts the rock on top.
Then it hits the clam on the rock.
This is hard work.
But when the sea otter
cracks the clam,
it will have something
good to eat.

A mother sea otter helps her
pup learn things.
She helps it learn to swim.
She shows it how to get to
the bottom of the sea to
look for things to eat.
She helps it learn what to eat.

Sea otters like to play in the sea.
They swim and play and have fun.

When the mother sea otters go for
a swim, the pups go, too.
The mother swims on her back, and the
pup rides on top.

The <u>Cake</u>

Come to my house,
Come up the walk.
Come in, have fun,
Come laugh and talk.

Play a little bit,
Eat ice cream, too.
Down the milk
I have for you.

Mom made a <u>cake</u>,
What will it say?
My name is on it,
And this is my day.

Now help blow <u>them</u> out,
Blow <u>two</u>, blow <u>three</u>.
But first make a wish,
Something good for me!

Chocolate What?

Mr. Green was a man who made chocolate for cakes.
One day Mr. Green was working with his big <u>pot</u> of chocolate.
Some of the chocolate ran out of the top of the pot.
The chocolate ran out of the pot and out of the room.
It ran down to the street.

104

Mr. Green could see a
milk truck across the street.

"Look out for my chocolate!" he said.

Mr. Snow <u>stopped</u> his milk truck.
A can <u>popped</u> out of the
back of the truck.
The top of the can came off.

Mr. Snow climbed out of the truck.
He put the top back on the can.
He did not see that some chocolate
had run into the can.

Mr. Snow went up and down the
streets in his truck.
The can with the chocolate inside
was on top of lots of ice.
Start and stop!
On and off!
Up and down went the truck's wheels.
The can rocked on the ice again and again.

Mr. Snow stopped the truck at his house.

"Hop in if you want a
ride, Maria," said Mr. Snow.

Maria looked for something to
sit on in her dad's truck.
She sat on a can and got off.

"This can is too cold to sit on," she thought.
"This ice makes things cold.
That can has some chocolate on it.
I think I'll look inside."

So Maria looked inside the can.

Something was inside the can.

"What can this be?" thought Maria.
"It is not chocolate.
It is not like milk.
It is too <u>wet</u> to be cake.
It is too hard to be milk.
I think I'll eat just a bit.
I want to know what it is."

Maria had just a bit.
It was cold, and it was good.

When the truck stopped, Maria showed
the can to her dad.

"Eat some," Maria said.
"It is a surprise.
It is good."

"What is it?" asked Mr. Snow.

"It is something cold, hard, and <u>wet</u>.

It is something like chocolate," said Maria.

Mr. Snow had some.

"It is good!" he said.

"Do you know what it is?" he asked.

"I think I do now," said Maria.

"I will name it chocolate ice cream."

Connie Chung

If you put on the TV at night, you
could see and hear Connie Chung.
She works on TV, and
she helps us find out the news.

In one day she will go and talk to many
people to get a big news story.
Some days she talks to children and
finds out what they want to know.
When she has a good news story, she
is on the news at night.

One way Connie finds out the news
is by talking to people on the telephone.
This is a good way to find out what
people know.

But if Connie wants the news story to be
on TV, she has to get pictures, too.
So she has to go and see the people.
When she talks to them, she gets the
pictures to show on the news that night.

Connie learned how to be a TV newswoman
when she went to school.
But when she was little, she acted
like a newswoman.

She had four sisters.
If Connie started to talk, her
four sisters talked, too.
No one could hear Connie.
So Connie made people hear her by going
up to them and asking them things.

Now people hear what Connie has to say.

And people want to talk to her.

Some people stop her when she is going

back to her house at night.

"You are Connie Chung," they say.

"I see you on TV."

There is something they want to know.

"What do you look at on TV?" they ask.

Connie will say, "The news!"

Collection 4

Words You Can Read

bear

city

claw

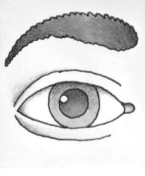

eye

hamburger

head

marks

mountain

squirrel

a	e	i	u	o
grass	legs	sticks	nuts	hot
pan	hen	miss	cut	
caps		pick	duck	

hard + er   harder

cut + out   cutout

cup + cake   cupcake

hen + house   henhouse

I'm really not lazy

I'm not!

I'm not!

It's just that I'm thinking

And thinking

And thinking

A lot!

It's true I don't work
But I can't!
I just can't!
When I'm thinking
And thinking
And thinking
A lot!

120

Indian School

The rain came down.
David looked out at it.
He was an Indian.
He was very, very sad.

"I wish I did not live in
a big <u>city</u>," David thought.

David's mother was an Indian woman.

She said, "You are sad.
I see rain in your <u>eyes</u>.
Do you want to talk?"

David looked at his mother.

"It's true that I am sad," he said.
"I really don't like school.
And I don't like this old house.
I don't like this old <u>city</u>."

"I want to play in the grass," said David.
"I want to climb way over the rocks.
I want to hear the animals at
night again."

His mother said, "David, don't
forget something.
You are going to a new school.
The name of the school is Pa-Ja-Chi."

"You will learn about the way Indians
do things," said his mother.

"Your dad and I came to this city
to look for work.
But we like true Indian things and
true Indian thoughts.
We do not forget them.
We want you to know about them
and to like them, David."

David started at the new school.
He learned things about Indian people.
He learned ways to make Indian things.
He learned about the animals.

One day his mother and
his big sister came to the school.
His sister talked to the children.
She acted out a story about
an Indian who made a bridge.
The story made the children laugh.
David was happy.

One day David's grandmother
went to see the school.
She said it was
a very good school.

She looked at David and
said, "Work hard.
Don't forget!"

David said, "I will not, Grandmother.
The things I learn here will help me.
They will help me like my school.
They will help me like the city."

David's mother said,
"I know you are happy.
Now I don't see
rain in your <u>eyes</u>."

One for You

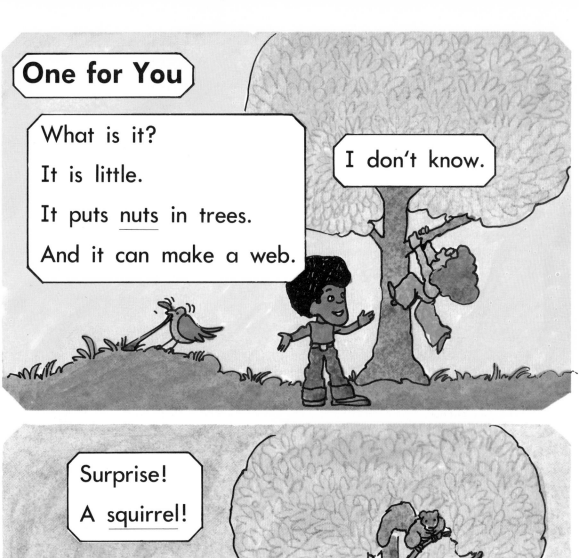

What is it?

It is little.

It puts <u>nuts</u> in trees.

And it can make a web.

I don't know.

Surprise!

A <u>squirrel</u>!

127

128

But a squirrel does not have two hands. And it does not live on a bridge.

True.
I know it does not.
I put all that in to make it harder!

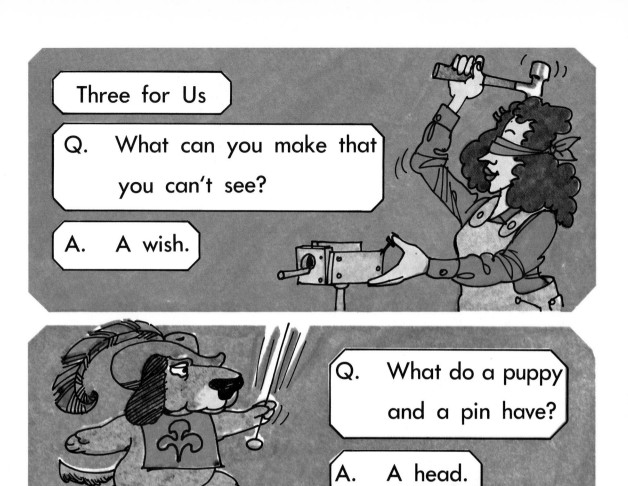

Three for Us

Q. What can you make that you can't see?

A. A wish.

Q. What do a puppy and a pin have?

A. A <u>head</u>.

Q. People ask where you are. Then they step on you and go across you. What are you?

A. A street.

Putting on a Play

Everyone likes to see a play.
If you want to have a play, you can.
This is the way to do it.

Make up a story.

Make cutouts of the heads of the
people and the animals in the story.
Put the cutouts on sticks, and
put your hands in socks.

Now sit in back of something.
Let just your hands in the socks and
the cutout heads show over the top.
Read your story and
move the cutouts.

Now you have a play.

Tracks

Here is a cat, and here is a puppy.

Here is a <u>pan</u> for the cat.

Here is a pan for the puppy.

The cat's pan had milk in it.

The puppy's pan had <u>hamburger</u> in it.

Who had the milk?

Who had the hamburger?

Look and see.

Look at the tracks that go
to the cat's <u>pan</u>.
They were made by an
animal that has four feet.

And you see <u>claw</u> tracks.

A cat has four feet and claws.
But so does a puppy.

Look at a cat walk.

A cat walks on four feet.

But the tracks of the back feet

go on the tracks of the front feet.

So a cat's tracks look like the

tracks of an animal with two legs.

A cat's <u>claws</u> are pulled
in when it walks.
There are no claw
<u>marks</u> in the tracks a cat makes.

Look at the tracks to the puppy's pan.
There are no claw marks.

Now do you know?

Who had the milk?

Who had the hamburger?

A Picture for Me

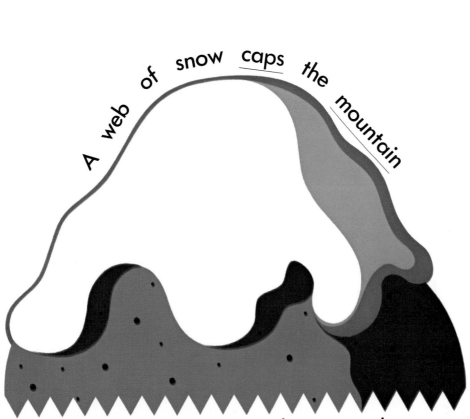

A web of snow caps the mountain

Like ice cream on a hot cupcake.

139

Sabrina

It was the first day of school, and
Sabrina was happy.
When Miss Potter said the names of
the children, they said "Here."
When she said Sabrina's name, everyone
looked at Sabrina.

Her name was different.

There were some Michaels and Lisas and

Susans and a David and an Amy.

But no one had a name like Sabrina.

"I will not come back," Sabrina thought.
"I don't like this school and everyone in it.
I'll make my name Susan or
Lisa and go to a different school."

"What is it?" said <u>Miss</u> Potter.
"Why are you looking like that?"

"Miss Potter, I don't want my
name to be Sabrina.
I want my name to be Susan."

"Then I want to be Sabrina," said Amy.

"Me, too," said Susan.

"No, Susan, I said it first," said Amy.

"Amy, she <u>picked</u> my name,
so I will get her name," said Susan.

"I want the name," said Amy.

"No, I want it," said Susan.

"Why don't we let Sabrina
say who gets the name?" said Miss Potter.

"If you give me your name, you can
play with my <u>duck</u>," said Susan.

"If you let me have it, you can play with my kitty," said Amy.

"Who said I wanted to give my name away?" said Sabrina. "Who would give away a beautiful name like Sabrina?"

Marks in the Snow

Joe and his sister, Debbie, were
not far from the house.
They looked up at the snow way
off on the mountain.

"It's really beautiful," said Joe.
"Do you think it looks that
   beautiful in back of the mountain?"

"I don't know," Debbie said.
"It would be fun to go and
see if it is different.
I would really like to see what
it's like across that mountain."

146

"Dad is across
that mountain now," Joe said.
"He is looking for a <u>bear</u>.
Many people are looking for it.
They are looking for the
marks of its claws."

"I wish Dad would say
that we could go, too," said Debbie.
"It would be fun to track a big bear."

"You know that we can't," said Joe.
"Everyone knows tracking <u>bears</u> is
  something children can't do."

"I know that is true," Debbie said.
"But I think it would really be fun."

Just then they were by the <u>henhouse.</u>
They had a surprise.

"Look at those tracks!" said Debbie.

"Where?" asked Joe.

"At the side of the henhouse.
They look like bear
tracks to me!" said Debbie.

"They could be," said Joe.

"I know they are from a bear!" said Debbie.
"I can read bear tracks.
 Dad showed us what bear tracks look like.
 I don't forget things like that!"

"They could be from a
 bear at that," said Joe.
"What can we do?"

"Dad said not to
look for the bear," Debbie said.
"But that bear can't be far away from here.
We can telephone the people who
are tracking the bear.
Then we can go and see if we can
find some tracks on the other side!"

"OK!" said Joe.

They went flying to the house to telephone.
Then they went out to
look for tracks again.
There were no tracks on the other side.

That night Dad came back.

"I hear you two had a big day," he said.
"You let everyone know that the bear
was not far away from here.
So they tracked it down.
Now people don't have to be afraid.
Everyone said you were a big help.
You two can really read tracks."

"Finding the bear tracks was
fun, Dad," said Debbie.
"But finding the tracks not
far away from
the house was really
a surprise."

A bear went over the mountain,

A bear went over the mountain,

A bear went over the mountain

To see what he could see!

The other side of the mountain,
The other side of the mountain,
The other side of the mountain
Was all that he could see.

Sad or Happy?

"What can we
do now?" said Roberto.

He looked at Pablo to see if he
could think of something different.

"I can't think of
one thing," said Pablo.
"I wish this was a school day.
Then I would be doing something."

"I know!" said Roberto's sister, Ana.
"Why can't we put on a play?"

"Good!" said Pablo.
"It will be fun to give a play!
We can all act in it."

156

"We can put on big
hats or a red sock and
a green sock.
We can make people
laugh," said Pablo.

"But I want to play an
old woman," said Ana.
"I want to be an
old woman who is sad.
That will be
beautiful in a play!"

"That is true, but it will be a
sad play," said Pablo.
"I want to put on a show that
will make people laugh.
Your play will make the people cry."

"Let me do this one," said Ana.
"You can read it and
say how you like it."

"OK," said Roberto.
"But Pablo and I will
make up the next play.
I'll act in your play."

"Me, too," said Pablo.
"Don't forget!"

So Ana made up a story about
an old woman.
She handed it to Pablo and Roberto.

"You can read it now," she said.
"I think you will like it."

And they did.

The three of
them worked hard for
two days learning what
they had to say.

The next night the people
came to see the play.
Grandmother Díaz came, too.
Pablo, Ana, and Roberto put on big hats.

Ana was going to be the
first to say something.
She was going to be a very sad woman.
She started to climb up in
front of the people.
But her hat came
down over her head.
It was over her eyes.
She could not see.

Down she went.
Her feet went one way.
Her hands went the other way.
Everyone laughed, and so did Ana.